THE CHRISTMAS COAT

Written By: Tracé Wilkins Francis
Illustrated by: HH-Pax

Annie Jean Publishing

The Real Life Adventures Of

Jo Jo Bean

Copyright © 2019, 2014 Tracé Wilkins Francis

ISBN 978-0-578-58975-6

Library of Congress Control Number: 2019915831

Printed in the U.S.A.

Annie Jean Publishing, Inc.
New York

email: anniejeanpublishing@gmail.com

Summary: Jo Jo Bean goes Christmas shopping with his daddy for gifts and meets a homeless boy who likes the same things he does. Through his new friend, Jo Jo Bean learns about Christmas joy.

Christmas was Jo Jo Bean's favorite holiday. He loved:

looking at the decorations;
decorating the Christmas tree;
baking cookies for Santa;
AND MOST OF ALL
getting gifts.

This year, Daddy took Jo Jo Bean Christmas shopping to buy gifts for their family.

Jo Jo Bean was excited to go Christmas shopping. He knew he could show Daddy all the things he wanted for Christmas.

As Daddy and Jo Jo Bean entered the store, Daddy told him, "Jo Jo Bean, we are here to buy a gift for Mommy, Grandma, and Big D. We are not here to buy toys for you."

"That's not fair," Jo Jo Bean whined.

"Christmas is about sharing and giving gifts to our loved ones and those who are less fortunate," Daddy said.

Jo Jo Bean wasn't listening. He was too busy looking at the Ultimate Mighty Master Smasher Mega Fighter Car.
"Whoa, look at that!" Jo Jo Bean said as he put the car into the shopping cart.

There were so many toys to choose from. Big ones, small ones, shiny ones, and Jo Jo Bean wanted them all. Before he knew it, the shopping cart was filled with toys. Daddy looked back at the cart and scrunched up his face. He was not happy.

"Jo Jo Bean all these things in this cart are for you!"

"No they're not," Jo Jo Bean said. "This one is for Mommy, this one is for Grandma, and this one is for Big D."

"Mommy, Grandma, and Big D wouldn't want any of those things," Daddy said.
"Daddy you said it's the thought that counts. I thought they would like these gifts," said Jo Jo Bean.

Daddy frowned. "Jo Jo Bean, you put no thought into these gifts. I want you to put all these things back right now."

"That's not fair," Jo Jo Bean mumbled putting all the toys back on the shelves. As he put the last toy back, he saw a little boy shivering in the corner of the store. His clothes were old and torn.

"What's the matter?" Jo Jo Bean asked the little boy.

"I'm okay, just trying to keep warm," said the little boy.

The little boy hung his head low. "I don't have a house. I live in a shelter with my dad. We live there with other people who don't have a home like us."

"Do you have your own room?" asked Jo Jo Bean.

The little boy sighed. "We usually sleep in one big room with other people. I wish we had our own room. It's better than sleeping on the street."

Jo Jo Bean was sad for the little boy. All children should have warm clothes and a home. "My name is Jo Jo Bean."

"My name is Benjamin. It's nice to meet you. Hey, that's a cool coat you're wearing. Mighty Master Smasher is my favorite superhero!" he said smiling.

"Me too!" Jo Jo Bean said. He liked Benjamin a lot. Anyone who liked Mighty Master Smasher was a cool person.
"I have an idea. Do you want to come to my house and play superheroes?"

"I would like to, but can't. My daddy and I have to get back to the shelter before dark, or we won't have a place to sleep," said Benjamin.

"You can spend the night at my house," said Jo Jo Bean. Benjamin's smile disappeared. "I wish I could, but I can't. I better get going now."

Jo Jo Bean lowered his head, "Oh ok. Well, see you."
"Yes, I'll see you around," Benjamin said walking around the corner.

Jo Jo Bean ran towards him. "Benjamin, wait. I want you to have this," he said taking off his coat and handing it to Benjamin.

Benjamin hugged Jo Jo Bean. "This is the best Christmas present ever, thanks to my new friend." Benjamin ran out the door and walked down the crowded sidewalk towards his dad.

Jo Jo Bean looked up and saw Daddy smiling.
"Jo Jo Bean, I saw what you did. I'm so proud of you. Do you know what?"

"No, what Daddy?"

"I'm going to make you happy by getting you the Ultimate Mighty Master Smasher Fighter Car," said Daddy.

Jo Jo Bean gave him a big hug. "You're the best daddy in the whole world. I love you Daddy! Merry Christmas!"

Daddy hugged him back and kissed him on the head.

'Merry Christmas, Jo Jo Bean!'

BOOKS IN THE REAL LIFE ADVENTURES OF JO JO BEAN SERIES

Birthday Bubbles

Delectable Vegetables

Safety First

The Christmas Coat

Park Blues

If you are interested in purchasing this series for your classroom, school, or day care, please email *anniejeanpublishing@gmail.com*. We also do author visits with the characters.